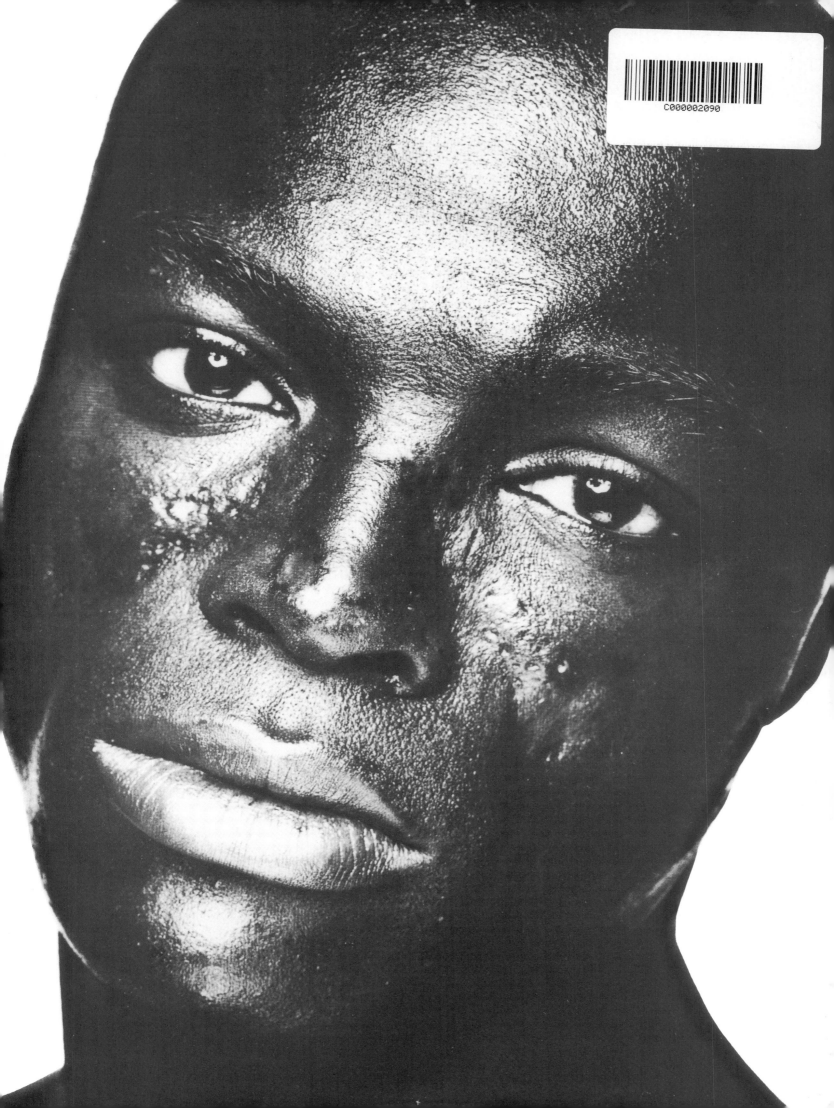

Exclusive Distributors:

Music Sales Limited
8/9 Frith Street, London W1V 5TZ, England.

Music Sales Corporation
257 Park Avenue South, New York, NY10010,
United States Of America.

Music Sales Pty Limited
120 Rothschild Avenue, Rosebery, NSW 2018, Australia.

Order No. AM92189
ISBN 0-7119-4315-X
This book © Copyright 1994 by Wise Publications.

Book design by Michael Bell Design.
Music arranged by Roger Day.
Music processed by Paul Ewers Music Design.

Your Guarantee of Quality:
As publishers, we strive to produce every book to the highest commercial standards.
The music has been freshly engraved and, whilst endeavouring to match the original running order of
the album, this book has been carefully designed to minimise awkward page turns and to make
playing from it a real pleasure.

Particular care has been given to specifying acid-free, neutral-sized
paper made from pulps which have not been elemental chlorine bleached.
This pulp is from farmed sustainable forests and was produced with
special regard for the environment.
Throughout, the printing and binding have been planned to ensure a sturdy,
attractive publication which should give years of enjoyment.

If your copy fails to meet our high standards, please inform us and we will gladly replace it.

Music Sales' complete catalogue describes thousands of titles and
is available in full colour sections by subject, direct from Music Sales Limited.
Please state your areas of interest and send a cheque/postal order for £1.50 for postage to:
Music Sales Limited, Newmarket Road, Bury St. Edmunds, Suffolk IP33 3YB.

Printed in the United Kingdom by
J.B. Offset Printers (Marks Tey) Limited, Marks Tey, Essex.

SEAL

Wise Publications

London/New York/Paris/Sydney/Copenhagen/Madrid

BRING IT ON

Words & Music by Seal, Gus Isidore, Wendy Melvoin, Lisa Coleman, Chris Bruce & Carmen Rizzo.

1. First I did-n't have the will to car-ry on
(Verse 2 see block lyric)

il - lu - sions in my mind.

Like that pic - ture when you feel you can't go on.

Like you've been left be-hind. Life goes on now,

Bring it on, bring it on,

don't wait un - til to - mor - row,

bring it on, bring it on,

1. bring it on.

2. bring it on.

Verse 2:
Give me something for the dream that I am in
You know I love the way you save me.
A broken pawn I depended on
It's only life I was feeling.
It goes on now,
Take me to that funky place where you and I were born.
Carry on now,
Ain't no reason you should feel for shorn,
Unconditioned love will bring it on.

Bring it on,
Bring it on,
Don't wait until tomorrow,
Wait until tomorrow,
Wait until tomorrow,
Bring it on.

PRAYER FOR THE DYING

Words & Music by Seal & Gus Isidore.

Fear - less—— peo - ple,—— care - less——

it goes on.

2.

space be-tween me and you,— there is a light_____ through that win-dow—

— hold on,— say yes, while peo-ple say no, life car-ries

on.

It— goes on.

I'm cross - ing— that bridge with les - sons I've learned,

yes while peo - ple say no. 'Cause life car - ries

on.

It goes on. It goes

on. Oh, oh,

life car - ries on.

Fmaj9

when no - thing else mat - ters,

Am9

when no - thing else mat - ters,

I just don't know what's got in - to me.

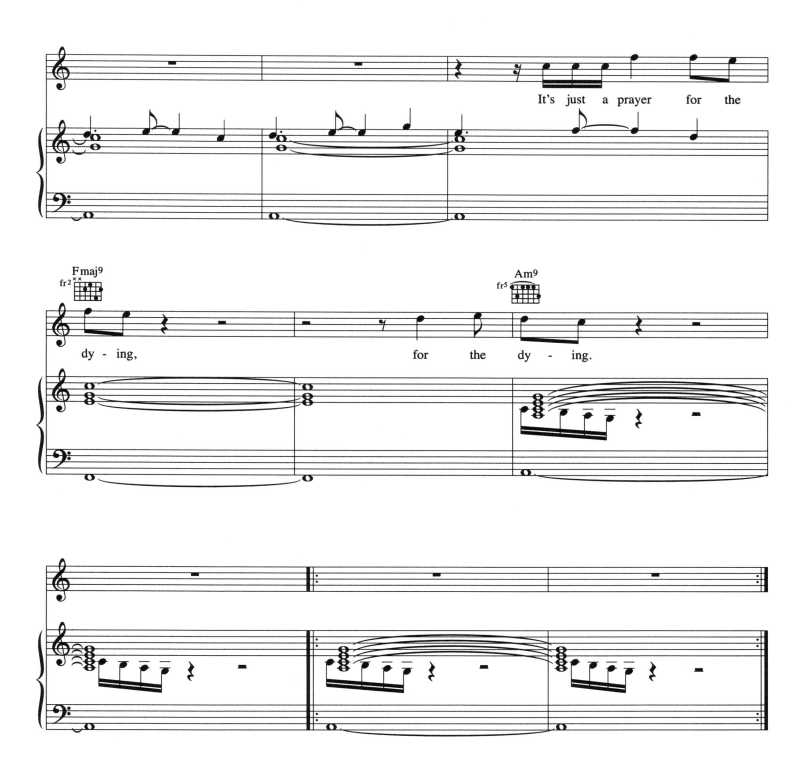

It's just a prayer for the dy - ing,

Fmaj9 Am9

for the dy - ing.

Verse 2:
Just say die and that would be pessimistic,
In your mind we can walk across water,
Please don't cry, it's just a prayer for the dying
I just don't know what's got into me.

DREAMING IN METAPHORS

Words & Music by Seal & Gus Isidore.

1. Love se - re - nade, soothe me with
(Verse 2 see block lyric)

morn - ing song. Help me find some - one

peace - ful and non judge-men - tal hold - ing me

back and make me feel whole with

21

play 1° only

(Well) Why must we dream in metaphors, try to hold on to something we

could-n't un-der-stand,— could-n't un-der-stand.—

And why— must we ar-gue loud-ly,

when peace— is our one sal-va-tion I could-n't un-der-stand,—

could-n't un-der-stand,— yeah.—

To Coda ⊕

1.

Verse 2:
Someone lost their faith
In seeking God,
So they turned to the needle,
Back to the cradle.
They were rocking it all too long,
Tell me what's going on
With your life -
Has it stayed the same?

DON'T CRY

Words & Music by Seal.

we were young___ and truth was pa-ra-mount___ we were
(Verses 2 & 3 see block lyric)

old - er then and we lived a life with-out___ a - ny doubt,___ those

me - mor - ies,___ they seem so long a - go,___ what's be -

come of them,___ when you feel like me I want___ you to know.___ Don't

Verse 2:
Today I dream
Of friends I had before,
And I wonder why
The ones who care don't call anymore.
My feelings hurt,
But you know I overcome the pain,
And I'm stronger now,
There can't be a fire unless there's a flame.

Don't cry, you're not alone,
Don't cry tonight my baby.
Don't cry, you'll always be loved,
Don't cry.

Verse 3:
The challenges we took
Were hard enough,
They get harder now,
Even when we think that we've had enough.
Don't feel alone
'Cause it's I you understand.
I'm your sedative,
Take a piece of me whenever you can.

Don't cry, you're not alone, *(Don't be so hard on yourself)*
Don't cry tonight my baby. *(Those tears are for someone else)*
Don't cry, you'll always be loved, *(I hear your voice on the phone)*
Don't cry, tonight sweet baby. *(I hear you feel so alone)*

FAST CHANGES

Words & Music by Seal & Gus Isidore.

1. May-be if I searched my
2. Now may-be if I took the

mind a lit-tle,   I'd come a-cross the rea-son
time a lit-tle,   then may-be I would know

Well here we are in se- parate rooms.

I can hear you {sigh - ing, cry - ing,} say- ing "No way out"

or so it seems, dry your eyes, we're fly - ing straight on through that win - dow.

Fast chan - ges ar - riv - ing,

36

KISS FROM A ROSE

Words & Music by Seal.

sea,— you—— be-came the light on the dark side of

me,— but love—— re-mains a drug that's the high and not the

pill— but did you know that when it snows, my eyes be-come large and the

light that you shine can't be seen. Ba -

da ba ya ya, ba ya ya ba da ba da da da ba ya ya.

2. There ___ is so much a man can tell you, so much he can

say, ___ you ___ re - main my po - wer, my plea - sure, my pain. Ba - by, ___ to

me you're like a grow - ing ad - dic - tion that I can't de - ny. Won't you tell me, is that

ny. Now won't you tell me, is that health-y ba - by. But did you

know that when it snows, my eyes be-come large and the light that you shine can't be

D.%. al Coda   ⊕ **Coda**

seen. Ba -   da. Now that your rose is in bloom, a

light hits the gloom—— on—— the—— bay.

PEOPLE ASKING WHY

Words & Music by Seal

1. Why
(Verses 2 & 3 see block lyric)

am I chang - ing?

Why do peo - ple _____

get com - pla - cent with the things they're told?

World dis - as - ters they come and go,

D.%. al Coda

⊕ *Coda*

How do I get___ to   where___ I've come___ from   now,_____

how will I paint___ this gar - den I've des - troyed green?_____

Can I get back___ to where___ I've come___ from 'cause there are peo-

-ple who be - lieve_____ in.

How do I get___ to where___ I've come___ from now,_____

Verse 2:
Life gets confusing but I don't know why
But I've made my plans already, having trouble with it all my life,
World disasters they come and go,
I'd give all my strength just to be back home.

Verse 3:
How do we get to where we come from,
Peace and love ain't enough these days.
Evolution says time is running out
We've been here too long.

IF I COULD

Words & Music by Seal.

55

gon - na come___ for sure.___ 'Cause

I___ know that___ some day we're

gon - na end___ our war.___ If I___

___ could___ I'd make___

FINAL SECTION OVER FADE

NEWBORN FRIEND

Words & Music by Seal.

just like I should——do, but my

whole world———— slips a-way.

I live my life,——— I live it slow -

- ly, and I take my time———

I'M ALIVE

Words & Music by Seal, Gus Isidore, Wendy Melvoin, Lisa Coleman & Carmen Rizzo.

Fell on my feet this morn-ing, two an-gels heard me cry,—

74

BRING IT ON (REPRISE)

Words & Music by Seal, Gus Isidore, Wendy Melvoin, Lisa Coleman, Chris Bruce & Carmen Rizzo.

Ba ba ba ba ba ba da da

ba ba da da da da.

Oh

can't you   see it's on-ly life,   ba ba

ba ba ba ba,   ba ba da da da da   da.

So bring—— it on.

Da da—— da—— da.